# Reflections *from the* Heart

FATHER BRIAN D'ARCY C.P.

First published 2002

© This arrangement copyright Father Brian D'Arcy C.P.

ISBN 1 873223 09 9

Typesetting and design by Typecast, Galway

Printed in the Republic of Ireland by Leinster Leader Printing

Published by Boa Vista, 31 The Baily, Galway

# Introduction

For many years I have been presenting an hour-long programme on BBC Radio Ulster. It is mainly a music programme but when people sent me little verses I used them. They became known as 'Reflections' and were dotted among the music selections. The strangest thing happened. People took more notice of the reflections than the music. Every week I get about fifty or sixty requests for the reflections I've used. Occasionally, though, over a couple of weeks several hundred people could write for some reflections that was particularly meaningful to them.

With each letter the question was always the same. Can I get your reflections in a book? Until now the answer was no. I have gathered just a few of the more popular reflections into one collection.

Most of them are, as the title suggestions, 'Reflections from the Heart': simple thoughts which help people through some of the hurdles we encounter daily in life. I hope they do that for you.

It's best to read them one or two at a time. If you get something out of them, read them repeatedly. They are talking to you at a deep level. Stories and reflections very rarely unpack their meaning at a first reading.

One reflection is here for a different reason entirely. It's the famous 'Getting Dressed'. Over the past couple of years I'm sure I've had at least a thousand requests for the words. The author, Patsy O'Hagan, has very kindly given me permission to reprint it here. It is The Bard of Armagh's masterpiece and if you really want to understand it, you have got to hear Patsy perform it himself. That he does on an excellent cassette, *A Bit of Craic*, which is available from: Patsy O'Hagan, 160 Ardboe Road, Coagh, Cookstown, Co. Tyrone.

My thanks to all the people who sent in these reflections (believe me  there are many hundreds more which couldn't be included in this book). Where the source is known we have acknowledged it. I hope you enjoy a few of these.

I hope they give you a laugh and some consolation if needs be. You can always hear and read new ones, both on BBC Radio Ulster and in my column in the *Sunday World*.

**Brian D'Arcy**
**The Graan**
**Enniskillen**

✛ ✛ ✛ ✛ ✛ ✛ ✛ ✛ ✛

# FATHER BRIAN D'ARCY

Fr. Brian D'Arcy is based at The Graan in Enniskillen. He presents an hour-long radio programme every Sunday morning on BBC Radio Ulster. A regular guest on Terry Wogan's programme on BBC Radio 2, he is best known as a columnist with the *Sunday World*.

Born and raised in Fermanagh, he spent over 20 years as a priest in Dublin before serving at The Graan in Enniskillen and also at Crossgar, Co. Down.

# *Risk It*

To laugh is to risk appearing the fool.
To weep is to risk appearing sentimental.
To reach out to another is to risk involvement.
To express feelings is to risk exposing your true self.

To place your ideas, your dreams, before the crowd,
    is to risk their loss.
To love is to risk not being loved in return.
To live is to risk dying.
To hope is to risk despair.
To try is to risk failure.

But risks must be taken,
Because the greatest hazard in life is to risk nothing.
The person who risks nothing, does nothing,
    has nothing, and is nothing.
He may avoid suffering and sorrow,
    but he simply cannot learn, feel, change, grow, love,
    live.
Only a person who risks is free.

ANONYMOUS

# *A Prayer for the Stressed*

Lord grant me the serenity to accept the things
    I cannot change
The courage to change the things I can
The wisdom to be careful of the toes I step on today,
As they may be connected to the feet
I have to kiss tomorrow.
Help me to give 100% at work
12% on Monday
23% on Tuesday
40% on Wednesday
20% on Thursday
and 5% on Friday
And help me to remember
When I'm having a bad day
And it seems that people are trying to wind me up
It takes 42 muscles to frown
28 muscles to smile
And only 4 to extend my hand and smack them in the
    mouth!

# *Thank You*

I love you
not only for what you are,
but for what I am when I am with you.

I love you
not only for what you have made of yourself,
but for what you are making of me.

I love you
for the part of me that you bring out;
for passing over the many foolish and weak things
    you find in me
and for drawing out into the light
all the beautiful things only you could find in me.

You have done more for me than any creed.
You have made me feel my own goodness.

And all this you have done
with your touch,
with your words,
with yourself.
Thank you

Anonymous

# *Spot On!*

If you can start your day without caffeine,

If you can get along without pep pills,

If you can always be cheerful ignoring aches and pains,

If you can resist complaining and boring people with your troubles,

If you can eat the same food every day and be grateful for it,

If you can understand when your loved ones are too busy to give you any time,

If you can forgive your friends for their lack of consideration,

If you can overlook it when those you love take it out on you when through no fault of your own something goes wrong,

If you can take criticism and blame without resentment,

If you can ignore a friend's limited education and never correct him,

If you can face the world without lies and deceit,

If you can conquer tension without medical help,

If you can relax without alcohol,

If you can sleep without the aid of drugs,

If you can honestly say that deep in your heart you have no prejudice against creed or colour, religion or politics,

Then my friend you're almost as good . . . as your dog!

AUTHOR UNKNOWN

*To make it possible for everyone to come
to church next week we are planning a special*

# No Excuse Sunday!

1. Beds will be placed in aisles for those who say "Sunday is my only day for sleeping late".
2. Eye drops will be available for those whose eyes are tired from watching TV late on Saturday night.
3. We will have steel helmets for those who believe the roof will cave in if they show up for church.
4. Blankets will be furnished for those who complain that the church is too cold. Fans will be on hand for those who say it's too hot.
5. We will have hearing aids for those who say the preacher isn't loud enough and cotton wool for those who say he's too loud.
6. Score cards will be available for those who wish to count the hypocrites (Number now increased!).
7. We guarantee that some relatives will be present for those who like to go visiting at Sunday church times.
8. There will be microwave dinners for those who claim that they can't go to church and cook dinner also.
9. One section of the church will have trees and grass for those who see God in nature, especially on the golf course . . . at service times.
10. The altar will be decorated with a Christmas Crib and Easter Lilies, to create a familiar environment for those who have never seen the church without them.

*See you in church maybe?*

FROM NEW ROSS PARISH NEWSLETTER 1998

# *Getting Dressed*

If there's wan thing on earth that makes me depressed
It's sitting waiting on the wife getting dressed,
I swear, til watch her would drive you insane
Some of her antics I'll try and explain.

Now we're asked out til this fancy 'do'
And I'm sitting shining from my head til my shoe.
I've shampooed and I've shaved and had a wee shower
And done ye might say, in a third of an hour.

But Maggie, she's different I'll have ye know,
I can't think of a word that's slower than slow.
She won't have a shower in case she might slide.
So the bath is filled up and Radox applied.

She slaps and she splashes. She sings and she laughs
You'd swear a crocodile was let loose in our bath.
She rubs and she scrubs, and her hair, she got set
Is tied back with a scarf in case it gets wet.

Then she dries herself on four towels or more
And the powder she used is like snow on the floor.
I believe she's a magician because from a wee bag with a
    flap
Our Maggie can produce a full chemist's shop.

There's creams and there's lotions and colours so bright
And wee dainty paint brushes, boys it's a sight.
There's lipstick and polish and bottles of spray
And wee things to pull out those hairs that've turned grey.

Now her make-up is on and she's powdered her nose
But the worst bit of all is when she's choosing her clothes.
There's no saying on earth I bet will compare
As a woman complaining that she's nothing to wear.

Now in front of the wardrobe she laments and she whinges
And the bloody thing is stuffed to the hinges,
With dresses all sizes and colour so gay,
Some meant for the sunshine or a cold winters day.

So with wan hand on her hinch and wan on her chin
She examines the contents that's hanging within.
Then the clanging of hangers rings aloud in my head
As a dozen or so outfits are flung on the bed.

I just sit and say nothing for I know that it's best.
I'm sitting ready, she's the wan that's not dressed.
Now in front of the mirror she'll stand and she'll grin
The first wan tried on as she pulls herself in.

She'll pivot, she'll smile, she'll pose and she'll sway,
That doesn't look right, as she throws it away.
The next wan's the same, she tries then she throws,
Still complaining I've got no bloody clothes.

But now I'm convinced our Maggie's not wise
When she's picking her clothes, does she think of her size.
I just sit and watch, not wan word I have said
As another dress is flung on the bed.

It's maybe just me I'm easy depressed.
Is this the done thing when women get dressed?
She has me confused I'm in a terrible state
The 'do' was at nine, now it's ten and we're late.

PATSY O'HAGAN

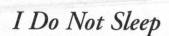

# *I Do Not Sleep*

Do not stand at my grave and weep:
I am not there, I do not sleep.

I am a thousand winds that blow,
I am the diamond that glints on snow,
I am the sunlight on ripened grain,
I an the gentle autumn rain.

When you awaken in the morning's hush,
I am the swift uplifting rush
of quiet birds in circled flight,
I am the soft stars that shine at night.

Do not stand at my grave and cry,
I am not there, I did not die.

# *Togetherness*

Death is nothing at all – I have only slipped away into the next room. Whatever we were to each other, that we are still. Call me by my old familiar name, speak to me in the way which you always used. Laugh as we always laughed at the little jokes we enjoyed together. Play, smile, think of me, pray for me. Let my name be the household word that it always was. Let it be spoken without effort. Life means all that it ever meant. It is the same as it ever was; there is absolutely unbroken continuity. Why should I be out of your mind because I am out of your sight? I am but waiting for you, for an interval, somewhere very near just around the corner. All is well. Nothing is past; nothing is lost. One brief moment and all will be as it was before – only better, infinitely happier and for ever – we will all be one together with Christ.

# I Am Living

Just to say that I am living – I am not among the dead
Though I'm getting more forgetful and confused inside
     my head.
I've got used to my arthritis – to my dentures I'm resigned,
I can cope with my bifocals – but I miss my mind!

— ✱ —

Sometimes I can't remember, when I'm standing by the
     stair,
Am I going up for something or have I just come down
     from there?

— ✱ —

It's not my turn to write to you, I hope you won't feel sore
     –
I think that I have written and don't wish to be a bore.
So remember that I miss you and wish that you were near
And now it's time to post this, and say goodbye old dear.

— ✱ —

Now I stand before the post-box, my face is really red:
Instead of posting this to you – I opened it instead!
Love from – oh this really is a shame:
I went to write my signature – and forgot my bloomin'
     name!

14

# *Joys of Old Age*

We old folk are very valuable:
We have gold in our teeth
Silver in our hair
Stones in our kidneys
Gas in our stomachs
And lead in our feet.

The other day the Minister came to call.
He said that at my time of life
I should be thinking about the hereafter.
I told him that I did that all the time,
Whether I'm in the kitchen or the dining room
Or the bedroom or the garden,
I stop and think: "What am I here after?"

# My Twelve Days

On the fist day of Christmas
My true love said to me:
"I'm glad we bought fresh turkey
And a proper Christmas tree."

On the second day of Christmas
Much laughter could be heard
As we tucked into our turkey
A most delicious bird.

On the third we entertained
The people from next door.
The turkey tasted just as good
As it had the day before.

Day four, relations came to stay;
Poor Gran is looking old.
We finished up the Christmas pud
And ate the turkey cold.

On the fifth day of Christmas
Outside the snow flakes flurried.
But we were nice and warm inside
For we had our turkey curried.

On the sixth day I must admit
The Christmas spirit died.
The children fought and bickered
We ate turkey rissoles fried.

# *of Christmas*

On the seventh day of Christmas
My true love he did wince
When he sat at the table
And was offered turkey mince.

Day eight, the nerves were getting frayed
The dog had run for shelter
I served up turkey pancakes
With a glass of Alka Seltzer.

On the ninth day our cat left home
By lunchtime Dad was blotto.
He said he had to have a drink
To face turkey risotto.

By the tenth day the booze had gone
Except for our home made brew.
And if that wasn't bad enough
We suffered turkey stew.

On the eleventh day of Christmas
The Christmas tree was moulting.
The mince pies were as hard as rock
And the turkey was revolting.

On the twelfth day my true love
Had a smile upon her lips:
The guests had gone, the turkey too –
And we dined on fish and chips.

# Who Am I?

I am more deadly than the screaming shells from the Howitzer.

I win without killing.

I tear down homes, break hearts and wreck lives.

I travel on the wings of the wind.

No innocence is strong enough to intimidate me, no purity pure enough to daunt me.

I have no regard for truth, no respect for justice, no mercy for the defenceless.

My victims are as numerous as the sands of the sea, and often as innocent.

I never forget and seldom forgive.

My name is Gossip.

MORGAN BLAKE

# New Life Acceptance Programme

1. I have a life-threatening problem that once had me.

2. Negative thoughts destroy only myself.

3. Happiness is a habit I will develop.

4. Problems bother me only to the degree I permit them to.

5. I am what I think.

6. Life can be ordinary or it can be great.

7. Love can change the course of my world.

8. The fundamental object of life is emotional and spiritual growth.

9. The past is gone forever.

10. All love given, returns.

11. Enthusiasm is my daily exercise.

12. I am a competent woman and have much to give to life.

13. I am responsible for myself and for my actions.

COURTESY OF WOMEN FOR SOBRIETY

# *Tell Me Now*

If with pleasure you are viewing
Any work that I am doing,
If you like me or you love me,
Tell me now.
Don't withold your approbation,
Till the Father makes oration,
And I lie with snowy lilies o'er my brow.

For no matter how you shout it,
I won't care much about it;
I won't see how many tear-drops you have shed.
If you think some praise is due me,
Now's the time to slip it to me,
For I cannot read my tombstone when I'm dead.

More than fame and more than money,
Is the comment warm and sunny,
Is the hearty warm approval of a friend,
For it gives a life a savour,
And it makes me stronger, braver,
And it gives me spirit right up to the end.

If I earn your praise, bestow it,
If you like me, let me know it.
Let the words of true encouragement be said.
Do not wait till life is over
And I'm underneath the clover,
For I cannot read my tombstone when I'm dead.

# How Often

How often do we think that God's not listening to our
   prayers?
How often do we feel neglected, feel that no one cares?
How often do we beg, beseech, for answers to our call?
How often do we think that there's no one there at all?

Do we never stop and thank the Lord for each new
   dawning day?
Do we never stop and thank Him for the friends he sends
   our way?
Do we never stop and thank Him for His beauty all
   around?
Do we never stop and realise, His loving knows no bounds?

Our every prayer is answered in the whispers of the wind.
Our every prayer is answered in forgiveness of our sins.
Our every prayer is answered in the blessings we can't see.
Our every prayer should simply be: "Thy will be done to me."

# *Difficult Things To Do*

To break a bad habit

To love an enemy

To live logically

To admit ignorance

To withhold judgement

To grow old gracefully

To persevere without haste

To wait without impatience

To suffer without complaint

To know when to keep silent

To be indifferent to ridicule

To concentrate in the midst of strife

To endure hatred without resentment

To fraternise without losing individuality

To serve without compensation,
commendation or recognition.

ANONYMOUS

22

## *My Prayer For You*

I said a prayer for you today
and know God must have heard.
I felt the answer in my heart
although He spoke no word.

I didn't ask for fame or wealth –
I know you wouldn't mind –
I asked Him for a treasure
of a far more lasting kind.

I asked that He be near you
at the start of each new day,
To grant you health and blessings
and light to show your way.

I asked for happiness for you
in all things great and small.
But it was His loving care
I prayed for most of all.

# *Time To Listen*

I tried to catch your attention each morning:

Remember when you came back to your seat and closed your eyes and put your head reverently down and talked; and talked and talked to me?

I wanted you to listen.

I wanted to tell you to open your eyes and look at my broken body, all around you.

I am your fellow parishioner, whom you meet every day in the street, and you ignore me, busy about your own concerns.

I am your next door neighbour, whom you spend so much time gossiping about and criticising.

And it sickens me, all the coldness, all the squabbling and diversions and those endless running battles,that scourge me, and crown me with thorns.

And then you pierce my side, at Communion, with your empty words of love.

If you love me feed my sheep and start in your own home.

Please don't keep me at bay any longer.

Don't talk to me – Listen.

I don't want you to on loving my spirit, and ignoring my body.

I don't want you to open your mouth, to receive my body and close your eyes and ears to shut it out.

Stop thinking of me as some kind of spiritual being in the skies.

I am one of these people, and you cannot have me without them.

On the last day, I won't ask you how many times you attended church – that is not your holiness.

I will ask you how your own community, family and neighbours fared?

How they grew in love and faith?

How did they live their prayer?

How did your community spread its love within your house, and across your neighbourhood?

Please open your eyes and ears and make time to Listen.

## *Money Won't Buy . . .*

Money will buy . . .

A bed but not sleep

Books but not brains

Food but not appetite

Medicine but not health

Fashion but not beauty

Amusement but not happiness

A house but not a home.

*It really is true that the best things in life are free.*

# *Prayer for a Newly Married Couple*

Lord, we two want to bring our life together with you,
and we want always to continue it with you.

Help us never to hurt and never to grieve each other.

Help us to share all our work, all our hopes,
all our dreams and all our joys.

Help us to have no secrets from each other,
so that we may be truly one.

Keep us always true to each other,
and grant that the years ahead may draw us
      even closer to each other.

Grant that we may pray together and love
      you in each other,
so that nothing may ever make us drift apart.

As we live with each other, help us to live with you,
so that our love may grow perfect,
a love that is patient and kind,
a love that does not insist on its own way
a love that bears all things, believes all things,
hopes all things, endures all things.

Give us a love like yours,
A love that never ends.

# *Slow Dance*

Have you ever watched children on a merry go round?
Or listened to the rain slipping on the ground?
Ever followed a butterfly's erratic flight?
Or gazed at the sun into the fading light?

You had better slow down; don't dance so fast:
Time is short and the music won't last.

Do you run through each day on a fly?
When you ask, 'How are you?', Do you hear the reply?
When the day is done do you lie in your bed
With the next hundred chores running through your head?

You had better slow down, don't dance so fast:
time is short and the music won't last.

When you run so fast to get somewhere
You lose half the fun of getting there.
When you worry and hurry through your day
It is like an unopened gift, thrown away.
Life is not a race. Do take it slower.
Hear the music before the song is over.

You had better slow down, don't dance so fast:
Time is short and the music won't last.

# Open-mindedness

Closed-minded people put others down,
Open-minded people are tolerant and understanding.

Closed-minded people cannot see the good in people who
    disagree with them,
Open-minded people see some good in everyone.

Closed-minded people mind other people's business,
Open-minded people mind their own.

Closed-minded people are envious and jealous,
Open-minded people are contented and thankful.

Closed-minded people know it all,
Open-minded people realise how little we all know.

Closed-minded people belittle our cultures and customs,
Open-minded people know the value of diversity.

Closed-minded people are suspicious and overly cautious,
Open-minded people are trusting and adventurous.

Closed-minded people talk without thinking,
Open-minded people think before talking.

Closed-minded people think they are always right,
Open-minded people realise how easy it is to be wrong.

Closed-minded people like to judge others,
Open-minded people let others judge them.

Closed-minded people form opinions without information,
Open-minded people value facts before opinion.

Closed-minded people are self centred,
Open-minded people put others before themselves.

Which are you – Open-minded or Closed-mined?

# *The Journey of Life*

*For each of us life is like a journey.*
*Birth is the beginning of this journey,*
*and death is not the end but the destination.*

*It is a journey that takes us*
*from youth to age,*
*from innocence to awareness,*
*from ignorance to knowledge,*
*from foolishness to wisdom,*
*from weakness to strength and often back again,*
*from offence to forgiveness,*
*from loneliness to friendship,*
*from pain to compassion,*
*from fear to faith,*
*from defeat to victory and from victory to defeat,*
*until, looking backward or ahead,*
*we see that victory does not lie*
*at some high point along the way,*
*but in having made the journey, stage by stage.*

ADAPTED FROM THE OLD HEBREW PRAYER

# Ten Commandments for Good Human Relations

1. Speak to people. There is nothing as nice as a cheerful word or greeting.

2. Smile at people. It takes 72 muscles to frown, only 14 to smile.

3. Call people by name. The sweetest music to anyone's ears is the sound of their name.

4. Be friendly and helpful. If you want friends, be friendly.

5. Be cordial. Speak and act as if everything you do is a genuine pleasure.

6. Be genuinely interested in people. Everyone has something likeable in them if you look for it.

7. Be generous with praise but cautious with criticism.

8. Be considerate of the feelings of others: it will be appreciated.

9. Be thoughtful of the opinions of others. There are three sides to every controversy – yours, the others person's and the right one.

10. Be alert to give help. What counts in life is what we do for others.

DE LA SALLE NEWSLETTER

# *Reflection*

Consider the benefits of choosing the optimistic route. The pessimists will see a glass filled to the halfway mark with water as being half-empty, the optimist, as being half-full. The optimistically creative person will see it as a vase for a rose bud, the optimistic pragmatist as a means of quenching thirst. And the optimistic priest as water to bless for baptism.

Consider the benefits of choosing the optimistic route as described in this poem.

*Two frogs fell into a deep cream bowl,*
*One was an optimistic soul,*
*But the other took a gloomy view.*
*'I will drown' he cried, 'and so will you.'*
*So with a last despairing cry,*
*He closed his eyes and said 'Goodbye'.*
*But the other frog, with a merry grin,*
*Said 'I can't get out but I won't give in.*
*I'll swim around till my strength is spent,*
*For having tried, I'll die content.'*

*Bravely he swam until it would seem*
*His struggles began to churn the cream.*
*On the top to the butter at last he stopped,*
*And out of the bowl he happily hopped.*

*What is the moral? It's easily found,*
*If you can't get out – keep swimming around.*

# The Flawed Life

It's strange how I'm made – half mystic and half nut;
My eyes upon the stars, my feet deep in the mud.
One moment I'm lying and the next I'd die for the truth!
One moment I'm kind, big-hearted, understanding, loyal;
The next, sneaky and cruel.
It's weird how a soul can be split up like this –
Part God, part scallywag.
It's inconvenient too,
Because you're never quite sure which part is on the job!

Once it used to get to me to be like that
I hated myself . . . I hated life.
I felt I'd been betrayed by God who's made me such a mess.
What was life worth if one was so full of flaws?
So strong, yet weak; philosopher and fool?
Yes, once because I could not be the perfect thing I wanted
    to be, I hated life.

Now, I know that flawed lives are good,
And serve a purpose in God's kindly plan.
Only those who've lived can feel a liar's shame;
Only cowards know the bitter blame cowards must face;
And only those who've failed can understand the fear of
    defeat.

So, through my weakness , I possess the key
To every heart that's sad, shamed and soiled.
Through my blunders, I've found tolerance and pity
In place of my lost pride.

So, God, I'm glad you made me as I am . . .
Mystic and nut, philosopher and fool.
my eyes upon the stars, my feet deep in the mud.
For I've learned that flawed lives can serve you well.

AUTHOR UNKNOWN

# NOTICE

## THIS OFFICE REQUIRES <u>NO</u> PHYSICAL FITNESS PROGRAMME!

*Everyone gets enough exercise*
*jumping to conclusions,*
*flying off the handle,*
*running down the boss,*
*knifing friends in the back,*
*dodging responsibility,.*
*passing the buck*
*and pushing their luck.*

# *Could You Just Listen?*

When I ask you to listen to me and you start giving advice,
you have not done what I asked.

>>>>>>>

When I ask you to listen to me
and you begin to tell me why I should not feel like that,
you are trampling on my feelings.

>>>>>>>

When I ask you to listen to me
and you feel you have to do something to solve my
    problems,
you have failed me, strange as that may seem.

>>>>>>>

Listen, all I ask is that you listen.
Advice is cheap.

>>>>>>>

When you do something for me
that I can and need to do for myself,
you contribute to my fear and inadequacy.

>>>>>>>

But when you accept as a simple fact
that I do feel what I feel, not matter how irrational,
then I can stop trying to convince you
and get down to the business of trying to understand it.

>>>>>>>

Irrational feelings make sense
when we understand what is behind them,
and when that is clear the answers become obvious

and I don't need advice.
If I want advice I will ask for it.

>>>>>>>

So please just listen.

>>>>>>>

If you want to talk,
wait a minute for your turn and I will listen to you.

## *My God Is No Stranger*

I've never seen God, but I know how I feel,
It's people like you who make Him 'so real'.

It seems that I pass Him so often each day,
In the faces of people I meet on my way.

He's the stars in the heavens, a smile on some face,
A leaf on a tree or a rose in a vase.

He's winter and autumn and summer and spring,
In short, God is every real, wonderful thing.

I wish I might meet Him much more than I do –
I would if there were more people like you.

# The Indispensable Man

Sometime when you're feeling important
Sometime when your ego's in bloom
Sometime when you feel that you
Are the best qualified man in the room
Sometime when you feel that your going
Would leave an unfillable hole
Just follow this simple instruction
And see how it humbles your soul!

~~~~~~~~~

Take a bucket and fill it with water,
Put your arms in it – up to the wrists
Take them out – and the hole that remains,
Is a measure of how you'll be missed!

~~~~~~~~~

You may splash all you please when you
enter,
You may stir up the water galore,
But stop – and you'll find in a minute,
That it looks just the same as before!

~~~~~~~~~

The moral of this is quite simple –
Do just the best that you can,
Be proud of yourself – but remember,
There is no indispensable man!

AUTHOR UNKNOWN

# *A Mother-in-law's Prayer*

Teach me to speak or hold my tongue:
Silence is divine.
Help me to pray to understand
This new found child of mine.
Keep me from taking bitter sides
Or feeding angry flames,
Help me to leave them both alone
Like children at their games.

Counsel me when to call on them
And when to say goodbye,
Instruct my heart to love them both
And not ask the reason why.
Teach me to be a friend in need
Whose smile they're glad to share
Never too near, yet never too far –
This is my humble prayer.

# The Tate Family

*Let me introduce you to the Tate Family. They are a big family and a very influential family, present in every parish and community group.*

✠ First there is **Dictate** who wants to run everything – usually does until there's nothing left to run.

✠ Then you'll find that **Rotate** will come in to try to change everything.

✠ But he will be blocked by **Irritate** who stirs up plenty of trouble with the help of his friend **Agitate**.

✠ Whenever there are changes to be made and new projects to got off the ground, **Hesitate** and **Vegetate** want to wait until next year or a more suitable time – which usually means sometime when they won't have to change at all.

✠ Very prominent in every community is **Imitate**, who wants everything to be run exactly the way he runs it.

✠ But the one that really upsets him is **Devastate**, who provides the voice of doom.

✠ Then there is **Facilitate**, who is most helpful when there is work to be done. In fact, **Facilitate** is the one who keeps the whole community going, always trying to keep the peace when everyone else is losing their head.

✠ There is always a battle between **Cogitate** and **Meditate** as to which of them will think things over more. Both of them are introspective and both of them think themselves wiser than they actually are.

✠  Finally, there's a member of the Tate Family that nobody wants to talk about, the black sheep. He's **Amputate** who has cut himself off completely from the rest of the family.

*The question we have to ask ourselves is this: which of the Tates are we? Or perhaps at different times in your life, are we all of the Tates?*

## *Everybody – Somebody – Anybody – Nobody*

There was an important job to be done.

**Everybody** was asked to do it.

**Everybody** was sure that **Somebody** would do it.

**Anybody** could have done it, but in the end **Nobody** did it.

**Somebody** got very angry about that because it was **Everybody's** job.

**Everybody** thought **Anybody** would do it.

But **Nobody** realised that **Everybody** wouldn't do it.

It ended up that **Everybody** blamed **Somebody** when actually **Nobody** had asked **Anybody**.

# The Devil's Beatitudes

✖ Blessed are those who are too tired, too busy, too distracted, to spend an hour once a week with fellow Christians in the Church – they are my best workers.

✖ Blessed are those Christians who wait to be asked and expect to be thanked – I can use them.

✖ Blessed are the touchy: with a bit of luck they may stop going to Church – they are my missionaries.

✖ Blessed are those who are very religious but get on everyone's nerves – they are mine forever.

✖ Blessed are the troublemakers – they shall be called my children.

✖ Blessed are those who have no time to pray – they are easy prey to me.

✖ Blessed are the complainers – I'm all ears for them.

✖ Blessed are you when you read this and think it is about other people and not yourself – I've got you!

# He Who Laughs Last . . .

*The following gems were gleaned from*
*Church newsletters in America.*

❋ Don't let worry kill you – let the Church help.

❋ *Remember in prayer the many who are sick of our Church and community.*

❋ For those of you who have children and don't know it, we have a nursery downstairs.

❋ *This afternoon there will be a meeting in the south and north ends of the Church – children will be baptised at both ends.*

❋ Wednesday, the ladies liturgy will meet. Mrs Johnston will sing *Put Me In My Little Bed* accompanied by the pastor.

❋ *Thursday, at 5.00pm, there will be a meeting of the Little Mothers' Club. All ladies wishing to be "Little Mothers" will meet with the pastor in his study.*

❋ This being Easter Sunday we will ask Mrs Lewis to come forward and lay an egg on the altar.

❋ *The ladies of the Church have cast off clothing of every kind. They can be seen in the Church basement on Saturday.*

❋ At the Evening Service tonight the sermon topic will be, "What is Hell?" Come early and listen to our choir practice.

# Prayer Before Exams

Lord, I come before you in need.
Exams are approaching,
and I am worried.

Give me courage
to face the coming weeks.

Concentrate my mind on my studies.
Help me to use my time well.

May I work hard,
but also rest and relax a little.

During each exam,
may what I studied appear on the paper.

May I read each question carefully,
identify what is asked,
and answer well.

When the result come
may I be satisfied
that I did my best.

May whatever path I choose in life
bring me happiness
and give me opportunities
to better the world.

Amen.

# *Tomorrow*

He was going to be all that a mortal could be –
    Tomorrow.
No one should be kinder nor braver than he – Tomorrow.
A friend who was troubled and weary he knew
Who'd be glad of a lift and need it too:
On him he would call and see what he could do –
    Tomorrow.

Each morning he stacked up the letters he'd write –
    Tomorrow.
And he thought of the folks he would fill with delight –
    Tomorrow.
It was too bad, indeed, he was busy today,
And hadn't a minute to stop on his way.
'More time I'll have to give others', he'd say – Tomorrow.

The greatest of workers this man would have been –
    Tomorrow.
The world would have known him had he ever seen –
    Tomorrow.
But the fact is he died, and he faded from view,
And all that he left here when living was through
Was a mountain of things he intended to do –
    Tomorrow.

ANONYMOUS

# A Good Marriage

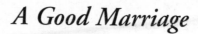

A good marriage must be created.

In marriage the little things are the big things.

It is never being too old to hold hands.

It is remembering to say, 'I love you', at least once a day.

It is never going to sleep angry.

It is having a mutual sense of values and common objectives.

It is standing together to face the world.

It is forming a circle of love that gathers in the whole family.

It is speaking words of appreciation and demonstrating gratitude in thoughtful ways.

It is having the capacity to forgive and forget.

It is giving each other an atmosphere in which each can grow.

It is not only marrying the right person.

It is being the right partner.

# *Rules for a Happy Marriage*

1.  Never be angry at the same time.

2.  Never yell at each other unless the house is on fire.

3.  If one of you has to win an argument let it be the other one.

4.  If you have to criticise, do it lovingly.

5.  Never bring up mistakes of the past.

6.  Neglect the whole world rather than one another.

7.  Never go to sleep with an argument unsettled.

8.  When you have done something wrong, be ready to admit it and ask for forgiveness.

9.  At least once every day, try to say one kind complimentary thing to your partner.

# *The Ship*

What is dying?
I am standing on the sea shore,
a ship sails in the morning breeze
and starts for the ocean.

She is an object of beauty
and I stand watching her
till at last she fades
on the horizon
and someone at my side says:
'She is gone.'

Gone! Where?
Gone from my sight – that is all.
She is just as large in the masts, hull and spars
as she was when I saw her,
and just as able to bear her load of living
freight to its destination

The diminished size and total loss of sight is in me,
not in her,
and just as the moment when someone at my side says,
'She is gone',
there are others who are watching her coming,
and other voices take up a glad shout:
'There she comes!'
–and that is dying.

BISHOP BRENT (1862–1926)

# Religion Class

*One day in Religion Class the subject was the Ten Commandments, and the class had reached the last one.*

When the teacher asked if anyone could state what the tenth commandment was, young Donald waved his hand wildly.

When asked he stood up proudly and gave his answer:

'Thou shalt not take the covers off thy neighbour's wife.'

\* \* \* \* \* \* \*

*Later, during a lesson on the story of the Prodigal Son, the teacher asked:*

'In the midst of all the celebration for the prodigal son, there was one for whom the feast brought no joy, only bitterness. Can you tell me who it was?

Donald was once again pleased to be asked and replied:

'The fatted calf.'

# *Myself*

I have to live with myself, and so
I want to be fit for myself to know.

I want to be able as days go by,
Always to look myself straight in the eye;
I don't want to stand with the setting sun,
And hate myself for the things I've done.

I want to go out with my head erect,
I want to deserve all men's respect;
For here in the struggle for fame and self
I want to be able to like myself.

I don't want to look at myself and know
That I'm bluster and buff and empty show:
I never can hide myself from me;
I see what others may never see.

I know what others may never know.
I never can fool myself, and so,
Whatever happens I want to be
Self-respecting and conscience free.

ANONYMOUS

# Forgiveness

O Lord,
remember not only the men
and women of good will,
but also those of ill will.
But do not remember
all the suffering they
have inflicted on us;
remember the fruits
we have brought,
thanks to this suffering —
our comradeship,
our loyalty,
our humility,
our courage,
our generosity,
the greatness of
heart which has
grown out of all this,
and when they come
to judgement
let all the fruits which
we have borne
be their forgiveness

A PRAYER WRITTEN BY AN UNKNOWN PRISONER
IN A CONCENTRATION CAMP AND LEFT BY
THE BODY OF A DEAD CHILD

# *Take My Hand, Lord*

I cannot pray, dear Lord, I cannot find
The hopes, recovery, health, and peace of mind.
So, take my hand, and take my feeble frame
And give me strength, and help me bear my pain.

I am so weak – give me the strength I need
To know that with your help, we will succeed.
So help me in these long and tiring days
To know that someone sings a song of praise.

The friends who care, who pray instead of me
For healing and a quick recovery.
So, take my hand, and let it cling to thee
And clinging – know no harm can come to me.

# Children Learn What They Live With

If children live with criticism, they learn to condemn.
If they live with hostility, they learn to fight.
If they live with ridicule, they learn to be shy.
If they live with shame, they learn to feel guilty.

If they live with tolerance, they learn to be patient.
If they live with encouragement, they learn to have
confidence.
If they live with praise, they learn to appreciate.
If they live with fairness, they learn what justice is.

If they live with security, they learn to trust.
If they live with approval, they learn to like themselves.
If they live with acceptance and friendship, they learn to
find love and God in the world.

ANONYMOUS

# A Dieter's Prayer

Bless my bathroom scales, O Lord,
Each week as I step on:
Help me lose a stone or two and not put any on.

Keep me from temptation, O Lord,
From chocolates and from chips:
Keep my will power going just in case it slips.

Help me count my calories, O Lord,
Steer me away from sweets:
Keep my stealthy palms away from naughty, fattening treats.

Keep me from the cake shop, O Lord,
Away from buns and crumpets:
And if a cake is in my hand give me strength to dump it.

Help me enjoy my salad, Lord,
My yogurt and Ryvita:
Help me to keep in mind one day my figure will be neater.

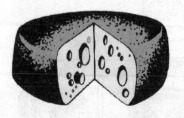

# *Methuselah's Menu*

Methuselah ate what he found on his plate,
And never, as people do now,
Did he note that amount of the calorie count;
He ate it because it was chow.

He wasn't disturbed as at dinner he sat,
Devouring a roast or a pie,
To think it was lacking in the right kind of fat
Or a couple of vitamins shy.

He cheerfully chewed each species of food,
Unmindful of troubles or fears
Lest his health might be hurt
By some fancy dessert;
And he lived over 900 years!

# *Take Time*

Take time to THINK:
It is the source of power.

Take time to PLAY:
It is the secret of perpetual youth.

Take time to READ:
It is the fountain of wisdom.

Take time to PRAY:
It is the greatest power on earth.

Take time to LOVE and BE LOVED:
It is a God-given privilege.

Take time to be FRIENDLY:
It is the road to happiness.

Take time to LAUGH:
It is the music of the soul.

Take time to GIVE:
It is too short a day to be selfish.

Take time to WORK:
It is the price of success.

Take time to do CHARITY:
It is the key to heaven.

# *Success*

Success is speaking words of praise,

in cheering other people's ways,

in doing just the best you can,

with every task and every plan.


It's silence when your speech would hurt,

politeness when your neighbour's curt.

It's deafness when the scandal flows

and sympathy with other's woes.


It's loyalty when duty calls,

It's courage when disaster falls.

It's patience when the hours are long.

# Happiness

Half the happiness of living
Comes from willing-hearted giving;
Comes from sharing all our pleasures
From dividing all our treasures.

And the other half is loving
First the Lord, then all things living
So, each mortal should be sowing
Love seeds while his life is growing
For all happiness in living
Comes from loving and from giving.

✛✛✛✛✛✛✛✛✛✛✛✛✛

# Giving and Forgiving

What makes life worth the living
Is our giving and forgiving.
Giving tiny bits of kindness
That will leave a joy behind us.
And forgiving bitter trifles
That the right world often stifles.

For the little things are bigger
Than we often stop to figure.
What makes life worth the living
Is our giving and forgiving.

THOMAS GRANT SPRINGER

# *Special Person*

God made every one of us
Then put us down on earth,
To see how we would make out
and how we'd show our worth.

He examines us occasionally
and looks at what we do,
Our kindness and honesty
So He must be pleased with you.

You do your best for everyone
You're there if they should fall,
And another thing about you
You seldom judge at all.

He's probably looking down
And He's bound to feel quite proud,
It's a cert He'll spot you right away
You stand out in the crowd.

# *Anyway*

People are unreasonable, illogical and self centred,
Love them anyway.

If you do good, people will accuse you of selfish, ulterior
    motives.
Love them anyway.

If you are successful, you win false friends and true
    enemies.
Succeed anyway.

The good you do today will be forgotten tomorrow.
Do good anyway.

Honesty and frankness make you vulnerable.
Be honest and frank anyway.

What you spend years building may be destroyed
    overnight.
Build anyway.

People really need help, but may attack you if you help
    them.
Help people anyway.

Give the world the best you have and you will get
    kicked in the teeth.
Give the world the best you've got anyway.

# When I Am Gone

When I am gone release me, let me go.
I have so many things to do.
Be happy that we had so many years.

*****

I gave you my love, you can only guess
How much you gave me in happiness.

*****

I thank you for the love you have shown,
But now it's time I travelled alone.

*****

So grieve awhile that we must part,
And bless the memories in your heart.

*****

I won't be far away, for life goes on,
And if you need me, call and I will come.

*****

Though you can't see or touch me , I'll be near,
And if you listen with your heart you'll hear
All my love around you, soft and clear.

*****

And then when you must come this way alone,
I'll greet you with a 'Welcome Home'.

# Grandchild

God sent us the rarest flower straight from his garden
    above,
He gave us a beautiful grandson to sprinkle our life with
    love.

He packs each day full with laughter, along with cuddles
    and good cheer.
It makes our day complete, just to know that he is near.

He loves all things of nature, animals and birds in the tree.
As he plays on the beach of Alvor, his happiness is a joy to
    see.
May your life be full of peace, along with happiness and
    good cheer
And if you ever need a friend, then we are always near.

Yes, by us, you will always be treasured
For the depths of our love can never be measured.
You chase away our clouds, brighten up our day.
Let's just say that we adore you, then there's nothing more
    to say.

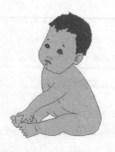

# *Don't Blame Me –*
# *Signed: God*

If you destroy this beautiful planet I made for you and the earth is scourged by your horrible weapons of war . . Don't blame Me.

#### \* \* \* \* \*

If you keep finding someone to hate, and a way to express that hate causes you to live in anxiety and tension . . . Don't blame Me.

#### \* \* \* \* \*

If you accumulate things upon things and then live in fear that you may lose them . . . Don't blame Me.

#### \* \* \* \* \*

If, by your unconcern and lack of compassion for the poor, your taxes are raised to help them . . . Don't blame Me.

#### \* \* \* \* \*

If you don't take some deliberate time to learn about 'Me and you' and 'you and Me' and consequently find your life confusing and doubt-filled . . . Don't blame Me.

#### \* \* \* \* \*

If you don't teach children by good example that 'gifting' their lives for others is the most noble thing they can do, and you end up with grasping politicians and exploiters . . . Don't blame Me.

# *Reflection*

Don't undermine your worth by comparing yourself with others.

It is because we are different that each one of us is special.

Don't set your goals by what other people deem important.

Only you know what is best for you.

Don't take for granted the things closest to your heart.

Cling to them as you would your life, for without them life is meaningless.

Don't let your life slip through your fingers by living in the past.

By living your life one day at a time, you live all the days of your life.

Don't give up when you still have something to give.

Nothing is really over until the moment you stop trying.

Don't be afraid to admit that you are less than perfect.

It is this fragile thread that binds us to each other.

Don't be afraid to encounter risks.

It is by taking chances that we learn how to be brave.

Don't shut love out of your life by saying it is impossible to find.

The quickest way to receive love is to give love;
The fastest way to lose love is to hold it too tightly;
And the best way to keep love is to give it wings.

Don't run through life so fast that you forget not only
    where you've been but also where you're going.
Life is not a race, but a journey to be savoured each step
    of the way.

## *Prayer for Discernment*

Grant me, O Lord, to know what is worth knowing,
To love what is worth loving,
To praise what delights you most,
To value what is precious in your sight,
To hate what is offensive to you.

Do not let me judge by what I see,
Nor pass sentence according to what I hear,
But to judge rightly between things that differ,
And above all to search out and do what pleases
You,
Through Jesus Christ our Lord.

# An Honest Prayer

*Dear God, So far today I've done OK.*

*I haven't gossiped, or lost my temper.*

*I haven't been grumpy, nasty or selfish.*

*But — in a few more minutes, God,*

*I'm going to get out of bed,*

*And that's when I will need your help!*

*Amen.*